ANIMAL ANAGRAMS

Each word below can be rearranged into the name of an animal.
How many critters can you find?

1. act
_____

2. low
_____

3. tab
_____

4. pea
_____

5. arm
_____

6. flow
_____

7. hear
_____

8. toga
_____

9. nails
_____

10. tutor
_____

11. reset
_____

12. barged
_____

Illustrated by Rosiland Solomon

Answer on page 47.

A HARD PUZZLE

You've got to really dig in if you're going to solve this puzzle. All the words have something to do with rocks and geology. They will all settle into the grid. Use the size of each word as a clue to see where it goes. All the words fit in only one unique combination.

3 Letters
Dig
Map
Oil

4 Letters
Base
Lava
Mine
Team

5 Letters
Erupt
Meter
Plate
Rocks

6 Letters
Energy
Hammer
Strata

7 Letters
Fossils
Igneous
Seismic

8 Letters
Drilling
Explores
Mountain

10 Letters
Microscope

SWING FLING

How many differences can you spot between these two scenes?

Illustrated by Sherry Neidigh

MALT MAZE

Can you slurp through this malt all the way to the bottom?

Illustrated by Charles Jordan

Answer on page 47.

DIRECTIONAL DILEMMA

Even a wise philosopher would have a difficult time cracking this mysterious Far Eastern code. Match the symbols with the correct letters to answer the riddle below.

What happened when the man left Japan by mistake?

Answer on page 47.

9

TOTAL TURKEYS

Find three turkeys whose weights will total exactly fifty pounds.

Illustrated by Jeff Stahler

Answer on page 47.

INSTANT PICTURE

Fill in each space containing two dots to see a horse that never races.

HIDDEN PICTURES

There are at least 25 objects hidden in this picture.
How many can you find?

Illustrated by Joe Boddy

POSTAL PUZZLER

The nicknames of various states are posted at the bottom. Fill in this grid with the postal abbreviation for each of these states.

Across

1. Tarheel State
3. Land of Opportunity
5. Hawkeye State
7. Sunflower State
9. Centennial State
11. Aloha State
13. Silver State
15. Grand Canyon State

Down

2. Golden State
4. Ocean State
6. Last Frontier
8. Palmetto State
10. Buckeye State
12. Hoosier State
14. Old Dominion State

Answer on page 47.

Illustrated by Ann Matsick

CHUCK WAGON MEMORIES

Take a long look at this picture. Try to remember everything you see in it. Then turn the page and try to answer some questions without looking back at the picture.

Illustrated by John Nez

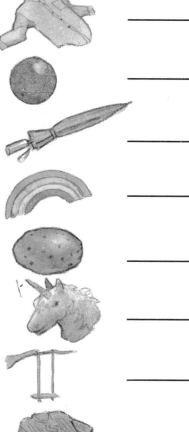

DON'T READ THIS UNTIL YOU HAVE LOOKED AT "Chuck Wagon Memories—Part 1" ON PAGE 15.

CHUCK WAGON MEMORIES Part 2

Can you answer these questions about the scene you saw? Don't peek!

1. How many cows were in the scene? 4
2. How many people were riding horses? 1
3. What animal, other than the cows and horse, was in the scene? 1
4. How many people wore mustaches?
5. What color neckerchief was the girl wearing?
6. What symbol was on the wagon?
7. What name was on the cook's hat?
8. What kind of food was being served?

Answer on page 48.

THE CAT'S MEOW

Beside each picture below, write the first letter of its name. Read down to find out what you get if you feed a lemon to your cat.

Answer on page 48.

Illustrated by Anni Matsick

DOT MAGIC

Connect these dots from 1 to 45 to find
a safe place to get out of the storm.

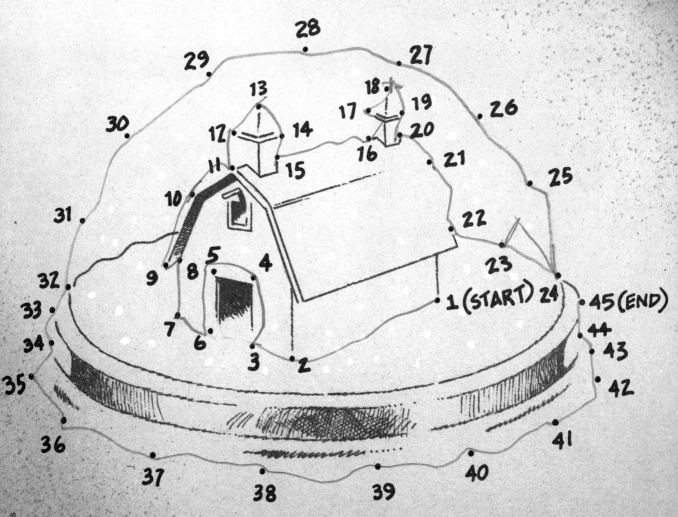

Illustrated by Tom Powers

GLOBE PROBE

That world-famous adventurer, Cincinnati Holmes, is off again. He's supposed to go to a number of countries on his latest tour, but the ticket computer malfunctioned and scrambled the names of all the places he's scheduled to visit. Can you unscramble the names of each place and point Cincy in the right direction?

1. LIZARB _____

2. YANKE Kenia

3. ALSO Laos

4. GLAREIA _____

5. TRAINGEAN _____

6. NAJPA Japan

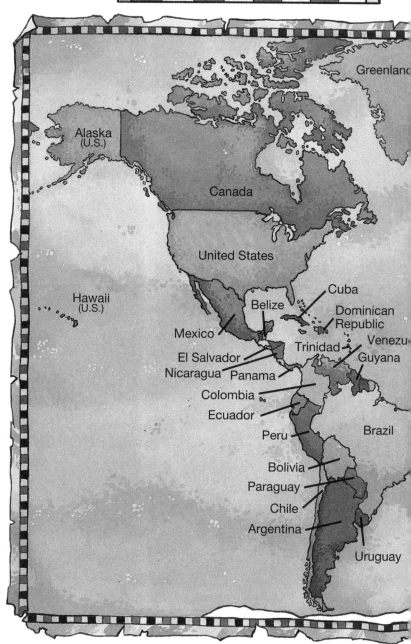

Illustrated by John Nez

7. DANIELC _____

8. XICOME _Mexico_____

9. TILAY _Italy_____

10. GOCNO _Congo_____

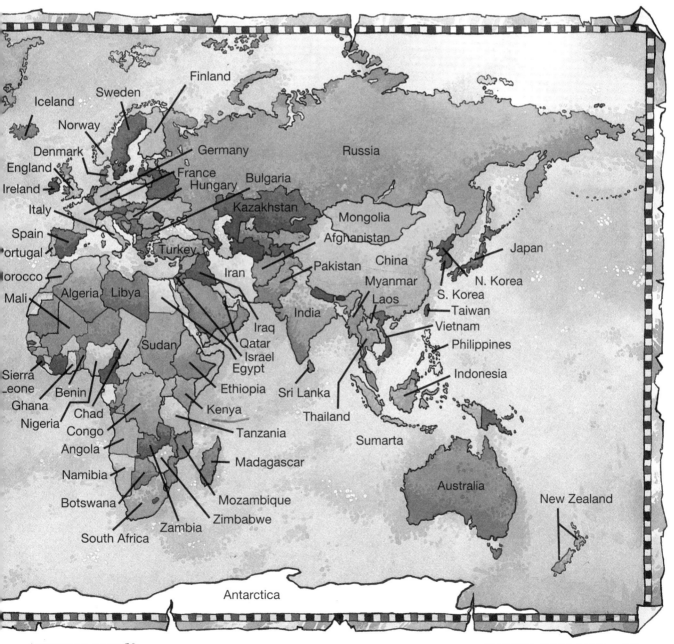

Iceland
Norway
Sweden
Finland
Denmark
England
Ireland
Italy
Germany
France
Hungary
Bulgaria
Russia
Spain
Portugal
Morocco
Turkey
Kazakhstan
Mongolia
Afghanistan
Iran
Pakistan
China
Japan
Mali
Algeria
Libya
Myanmar
N. Korea
S. Korea
India
Laos
Taiwan
Iraq
Vietnam
Sudan
Qatar
Israel
Egypt
Philippines
Sierra Leone
Ethiopia
Sri Lanka
Indonesia
Benin
Ghana
Kenya
Thailand
Nigeria
Chad
Congo
Tanzania
Sumarta
Angola
Madagascar
Namibia
Australia
Botswana
Mozambique
New Zealand
Zambia
Zimbabwe
South Africa

Antarctica

COOKIE COUNTER

Count the cookies and give the right amount for each statement below.

A. The total of all the cookies is _____.

B. ¹/₂ of all the cookies is _____.

C. ¹/₃ of all the cookies is _____.

D. ¹/₄ of all the cookies is _____.

E. If you and a friend ate all but three of these cookies, how many would be left? _____

Answer on page 48.

Illustrated by Jerry Zimmerman

WHAT'S IN A WORD?

Light the candles and get ready to sing. But before we open the presents, how many words of three letters or more can you make out of the letters in BIRTHDAY? We found at least 40.

Birth, day, Bay, Bit

Illustrated by R. Michael Palan

Answer on page 48.

RIDDLE ME THESE

Nine riddles and their solutions are included in this crossword puzzle. Filling in all the blanks will help you come up with the answers to the riddles.

ACROSS

* 1. What belongs to you that other people use more than you do?
* 5. What is it that most often becomes a woman?
9. Opposite of closed
10. Margarine
11. Directs a person, or something, to a certain place
* 13. What is alive, but has only one foot?
14. Abbreviation for point
16. Baby goats are called ki__ __.
* 17. Where can you find the most educated fish?
19. Abbreviation for company
20. Abbreviation for Oregon
22. The need to pay for something you bought
* 24. What is the best thing to put in a pie?
28. Kitten sounds or some London streets
30. A certain space, or region
31. To cook up a pot of tea
32. Past tense of ring

DOWN

* 1. What smells most in a bakery?
2. Large primate
3. Grown-up boys
* 4. What the mouse said when the cat caught him by his tail: "It's the __."
5. Opposite of stop
6. Sick, not feeling well
7. Tall grasses that grow near water
8. Abraham Lincoln was born in a cabin made of these.
12. Active recreation; game
15. Directional word, short for toward
17. Another name for a planter of grain
18. One of Santa's laughs
* 19. What has teeth, but never eats?
21. Coarse, long hair
23. A female sheep
* 25. What people and corn have in common (singular)
26. A period of time in history
27. The number following nine
29. Opposite of NE

Answer on page 48.

TRAVEL TROUBLES

How many unusual things can you see in this scene?

Illustrated by Randy Verougstraete

STOP, LOOK, AND LIST

Under every category, list one thing that begins with each letter. For example, one breakfast item that begins with "C" is Coffee. Can you name another?

BREAKFAST ITEMS

C _____

J _____

T _____

B _____

P _____

BIG CATS

C _____

J _____

T _____

B _____

P _____

SPORTS THAT USE BALLS

C _____

J _____

T _____

B _____

P _____

Illustrated by Lisa Dayer

Answer on page 48.

PICTURE MIXER

Copy these mixed-up squares in the spaces on the next page to put this picture back together. The letters and numbers tell you where each square belongs. The first one, A-3, has been done for you.

Illustrated by Tom Powers

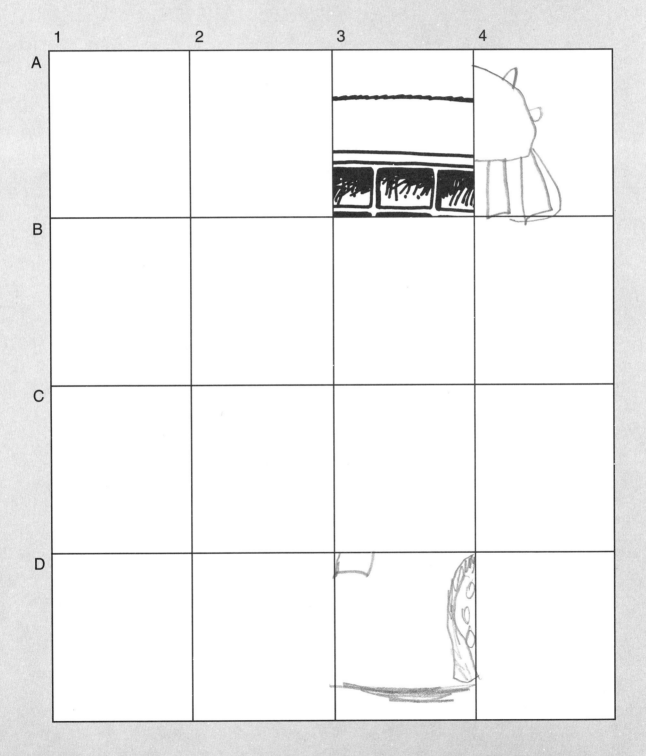

BLANK ACCOUNTS

Fill in each box below with the numbers 0, 1, 2, 3, 4, or 5.
No number may appear more than once in any row or column.

	1	2			
3			0	5	1
2		5			
		0			3
4	5			0	2
		1	2	3	

PPPPPSSST

BLANK BAG

THE NUMBERS GANG

Illustrated by Barbara Gray

   Answer on page 48.

THE KEY TO IT ALL

Alice has five keys. Each key is a different color and opens a different door. From the clues below, can you figure out which key opens which door?

Use the chart to keep track of your answers. Put "X" in each box that can't be true and "O" in the boxes that match.

	front	back	shed	car	office
gold					
blue					
red					
green					
purple					

1. The office key is a primary color.

2. No key color has the same number of letters as the door it opens.

3. The shed is green, and the key that opens it is not.

4. The blue key opens a house door.

   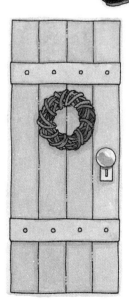 

Answer on page 48.

SPORTS PAGES

The names of 21 different sports are hidden on this field.
To get a good score and win, you must look up, down,
across, backward, and diagonally. Some letters will
appear in more than one word.

AEROBICS
ARCHERY
BASEBALL
BASKETBALL
BOWLING
CYCLING
DIVING

FIELD HOCKEY
FOOTBALL
GOLF
KARATE
LACROSSE
LUGE
POLO

RUGBY
SOCCER
SOFTBALL
SURFING
TENNIS
TRACK
WRESTLING

Illustrated by Mark Corcoran

```
A S O F T B A L L L B C F
L L A B T E K S A B Y L
G U E A S R N G F E C O
N H G S E U A N K L L G
I R J E V R R C I N I N
L L A B T O O F K S N I
W G R A Z H Y B I Q G L
O N C L D B O T I N U T
B I H L G X C L Y C G S
Z V E U L A C R O S S E
B I R E C C O S O P O R
F D Y E T A R A K D F W
```

Answer on page 49.

BEACH BUDDIES

Can you tell who left each set of tracks below?

Answer on page 49.

Illustrated by Anni Matsick

DO IT IN INK

Each word below ends with the letters I-N-K. Use a pen and these clues to fill in the rest of the letters.

1. Light red: ___ INK
2. Part of a chain: ___ INK
3. Place to skate: ___ INK
4. Sound that a pig makes: ___ INK
5. Place to wash your face: ___ INK
6. Small ferret-like animal: ___ INK
7. Do this with one eye: ___ INK
8. Do this with both eyes: ___ ___ INK
9. Beverage: ___ ___ INK
10. Do this with your brain: ___ ___ INK
11. On the edge of something: ___ ___ INK
12. Decrease in size: ___ ___ ___ INK

Illustrated by Gregg Valley

OUT OF THIS WORLD

Ride the spaceways as you try to solve the
riddle below. Follow the directions and
you'll have a safe landing.

Where do space travelers go swimming?

| 1 | 2 | 3 | 4 | 5 | 6 | 7 | 8 | 7 | 9 | 10 | 5 | 7 | 10 |

Letter five is on the moon.

Look right on your rocket for letter three.

The meteor storm contains letter two.

The flying saucer has letter four.

Letter one is on the planet with the red circle.

The rings around that planet hold letter six.

The stars form letter nine.

Letter eight is on the planet's surface.

The spacewalker has letter seven.

Look for letter ten in the Big Dipper.

LUCKY U

There are at least 23 horseshoes in this scene. How many can you find?

Illustrated by Kit Wray

TOURIST TRAP

The family is trapped in the center of a large amusement park. Can you help them find their way to the parking lot? They must stop at the restrooms and the drinking fountain on their way out, but they want to avoid all the other attractions.

Answer on page 49.

CLOTHES CALL

From each section, try to find one item that
matches the clothes these people are wearing.

Answer on page 49.

GUESS WHO

A mystery person can be found in the boxes on the next page.
Two of the characters he created can also be found there.

This person was born in New York City. This person was an essayist, historian, and one of the first of America's great writers. Some of this person's famous works were inspired by stories and legends told by Dutch descendants living in New York. This mystery person, using the pen name Diedrich Knickerbocker, wrote a history of New York. This book brought the word *Knickerbocker* into the English language. This mystery person is buried in Sleepy Hollow Cemetery.

Illustrated by Judith Hunt

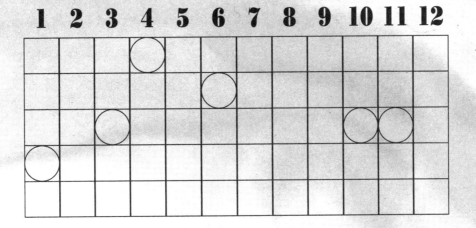

1	2	3	4	5	6	7	8	9	10	11	12

To solve this puzzle, write the 5-letter answer to each clue vertically in the corresponding number column.

When complete, and if done correctly, one character's name will be spelled out across the top row, and a second character's name will be spelled out across the bottom row. The author's last name will appear in the circles, reading from left to right.

1. Plural form of radius
2. Sir _____ Newton
3. Horizontal rod or branch that birds stand on
4. A stringed instrument slightly larger than a violin
5. In acting, to make up and perform something on the spur of the moment
6. _____ glycerin is used in making dynamite.
7. "Around the _____ in 80 Days"
8. Of or like an ion
9. Not ever
10. Nairobi is the capital of this country.
11. Boston airport
12. To wipe out

Answer on page 49.

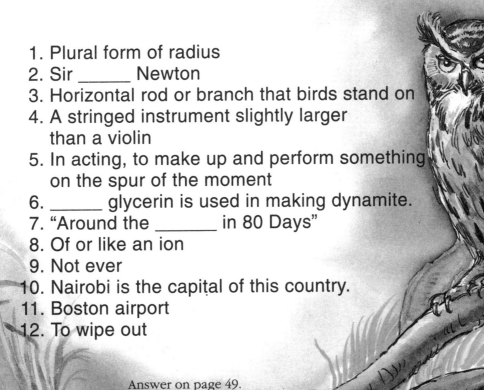

ROW, ROW, ROW

Each pumpkin below has something in common with the two others in the same row. For example, in the top row across, each pumpkin has a triangular nose. Look at the other rows across, down, and diagonally. Can you tell what each row of pumpkins has in common?

Answer on page 50.

WHAT'S YOUR SIGN?

Here's your chance to open your own business. Put a sign on this window giving your name and what kind of place this is. Will you open a pizza shop or a photo stop? It's up to you. Now get busy.

OUT OF TIME

We've arrived at this moment right on time, but a few objects seem out of place. Find at least 10 items that hadn't been invented or developed at the time this scene took place.

MAYFLOWER

10 Gal.

Pilgrims Plymouth

and at
Rock - 1620.

JACK AND THE GIANT

Number these pictures to show what happened first, second, and so on.

Answer on page 50.

ANSWERS

COVER

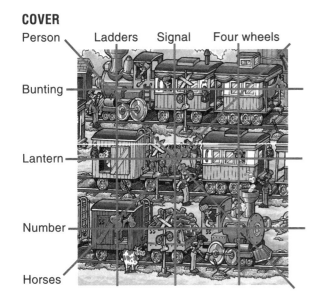

Person — Ladders — Signal — Four wheels
Bunting
Lantern
Number
Horses

ANIMAL ANAGRAMS (page 3)

1. cat
2. owl
3. bat
4. ape
5. ram
6. wolf
7. hare
8. goat
9. snail
10. trout
11. steer
12. badger

A HARD PUZZLE (pages 4-5)

MALT MAZE (page 7)

DIRECTIONAL DILEMMA (pages 8-9)

What happened when the man left Japan by mistake?
He was disoriented!

TOTAL TURKEYS (page 10)

Two possible answers are 14+12+24 or 37+12+1.

INSTANT PICTURE (page 11)

POSTAL PUZZLER (page 14)

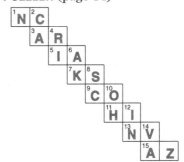

CHUCK WAGON MEMORIES (page 16)

1. 4
2. 1
3. dog
4. 2
5. blue
6. shamrock
7. Clem
8. peas

THE CAT'S MEOW (page 16)

What do you get if you feed a lemon to your cat?
A sourpuss.

DOT MAGIC (page 17)

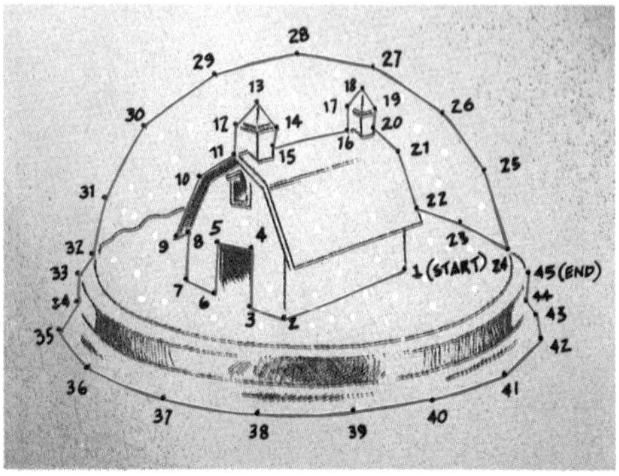

GLOBE PROBE (pages 18-19)

The answer appears on page 50.

COOKIE COUNTER (page 20)

A. 48 B. 24 C. 16 D. 12 E. 3

WHAT'S IN A WORD? (page 21)

We found 52 words. You may have found others.
aid, air, airy, arid, art, arty, bad, bait, bar, bard, bat, bath, bay, bid, bird, birdy, birth, bit, brad, braid, brat, bray, dairy, dart, day, diary, dirt, dirty, drab, habit, hair, hairy, hard, hardy, hart, hat, hay, hid, hit, hybrid, rabid, raid, ray, rib, rid, tab, tardy, third, tidy, tray, triad, yard

RIDDLE ME THESE (pages 22-23)

N	A	M	E	■	G	I	R	L
O	P	E	N	■	O	L	E	O
S	E	N	D	S	■	L	E	G
E	■	■	■	P	T	■	D	S
■	S	C	H	O	O	L	S	■
C	O	■	O	R	■	■	■	S
O	W	E	■	T	E	E	T	H
M	E	W	S	■	A	R	E	A
B	R	E	W	■	R	A	N	G

STOP, LOOK, AND LIST (page 25)

BREAKFAST ITEMS	BIG CATS	SPORTS THAT USE BALLS
Cereal	Cougar	Croquet
Juice	Jaguar	Jai Alai
Toast	Tiger	Tennis
Butter	Bobcat	Baseball
Pancakes	Panther	Polo

PICTURE MIXER (pages 26-27)

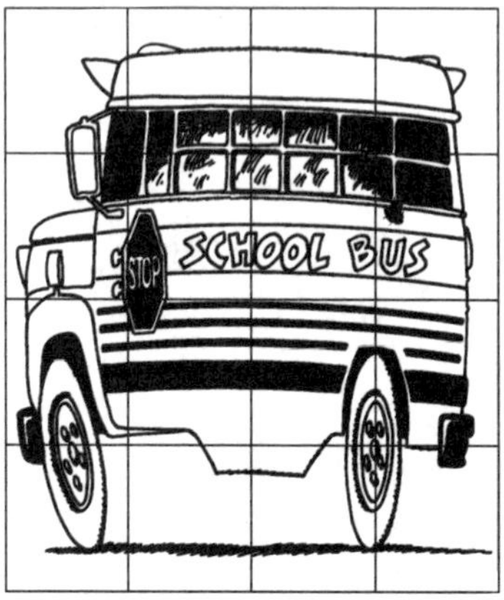

BLANK ACCOUNTS (page 28)

0	1	2	3	4	5
3	2	4	0	5	1
2	3	5	4	1	0
1	4	0	5	2	3
4	5	3	1	0	2
5	0	1	2	3	4

THE KEY TO IT ALL (page 29)

Clue 2 says no color or door have the same number of letters. So the front door is not green; the back door nor the shed door are gold or blue; the car door isn't red; and the office door isn't purple. Clue 4 says the blue key opens a house door. Since we know it's not the back door, blue must open the front. Red and blue are the primary colors here. Since the office door isn't blue, it must be red. By elimination, the car door needs the gold key. Of the remaining choices, we know the shed key is not green (Clue 3), so it must be purple. The green key opens the back door.

In summary:		
	gold	car
	blue	front
	red	office
	green	back
	purple	shed

SPORTS PAGES (pages 30-31)

BEACH BUDDIES (page 32)

DO IT IN INK (page 33)

1. Pink
2. Link
3. Rink
4. Oink
5. Sink
6. Mink
7. Wink
8. Blink
9. Drink
10. Think
11. Brink
12. Shrink

OUT OF THIS WORLD (pages 34-35)

Where do space travelers go swimming?
In the Galax-seas!

TOURIST TRAP (page 37)

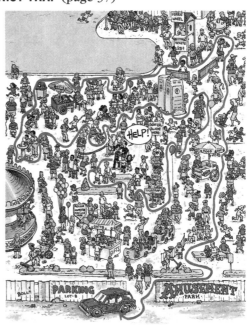

CLOTHES CALL (pages 38-39)

GUESS WHO (pages 40-41)

1	2	3	4	5	6	7	8	9	10	11	12
R	I	P	V	A	N	W	I	N	K	L	E
A	S	E	I	D	I	O	O	E	E	O	R
D	A	R	O	L	T	R	N	V	N	G	A
I	A	C	L	I	R	L	I	E	Y	A	S
I	C	H	A	B	O	D	C	R	A	N	E

Rip Van Winkle and Ichabod Crane are two characters created by Washington Irving.

ROW, ROW, ROW (page 42)

Leaves   Wink   One tooth   Eyebrows

Noses

Candles

Paints

Oval shapes

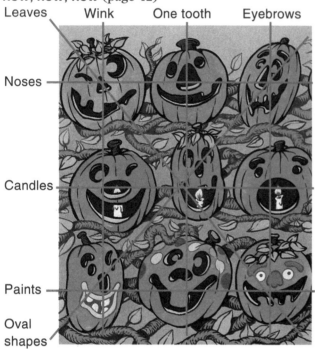

OUT OF TIME (pages 44-45)

We found these items. You may have found others.

1. Rubber tire
2. Book of matches
3. Rubber raft
4. Outboard motor
5. American flag
6. Canned soda
7. Butane burner
8. Plastic gas can
9. Crates
10. Barbeque grill
11. Baseball cap
12. Plastic dolls
13. Electronic games

JACK AND THE GIANT (page 46)

4	6
1	3
5	2

GLOBE PROBE (pages 18-19)

1. Brazil
2. Kenya
3. Laos
4. Algeria
5. Argentina
6. Japan
7. Iceland
8. Mexico
9. Italy
10. Congo

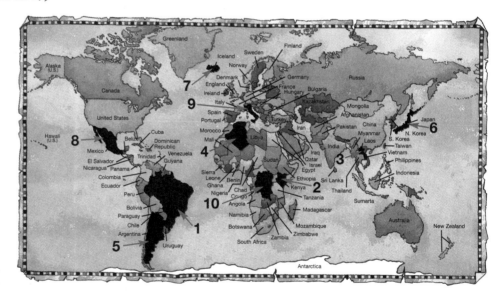

Editor: Jeffrey A. O'Hare • **Art Director:** Jeff George
Designer: Glenn Boyd • **Project Director:** Pamela Gallo • **Managing Editor:** Margie Hayes Richmond
Editorial Consultant: Andrew Gutelle • **Design Consultant:** Bob Feldgus

Puzzle Contributors
Samuel E. Backer • Madeline Cohen • Ann Fisher • Jeanette C. Grote
Susan C. Hall • Elaine Hilowitz • Eleanor Klein • Cari Koerner • Sue Macy
Dana Pratola • Jennifer Schulze • Sherry Timberman • Carol Upton • Charles Weaver